True Dog Stories

Stories

A Dolch Classic Basic Reading Book

by Edward W. Dolch and Marguerite P. Dolch

illustrated by Meryl Henderson

The Basic Reading Books

The Basic Reading Books are fun reading books that fill the need for easy-to-read stories for the primary grades. The interest appeal of these true stories will encourage independent reading at the early reading levels.

The stories focus on the 95 Common Nouns and the Dolch 220 Basic Sight Vocabulary. Beyond these simple lists, the books use about two new words per page.

This series was prepared under the direction and supervision of Edward W. Dolch, Ph.D.

This series was revised under the direction and supervision of Eleanor Dolch LaRoy and the Dolch Family Trust.

SRA/McGraw-Hill

*A Division of The **McGraw·Hill** Companies*

Original version copyright © 1958 by Edward W. Dolch.
Copyright © 1999 by SRA/McGraw-Hill. All rights reserved. Except as permitted under the United States Copyright Act, no part of this publication may be reproduced or distributed in any form or by any means, or stored in a database or retrieval system without prior written permission from the publisher.

Printed in the United States of America.

Send all inquiries to:
SRA/McGraw-Hill
250 Old Wilson Bridge Road, Suite 310
Worthington, OH 43085

ISBN 0-02-830809-3

2 3 4 5 6 7 8 9 0 QST 04 03 02 01 00 99

Table of Contents

My Name is T.J.

One day T.J. came to Brett and Jerry
in a big box. On the box in big, black
letters, the boys read,

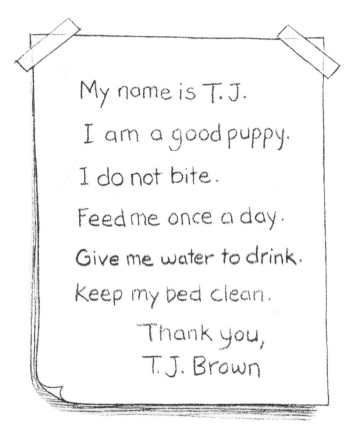

My name is T.J.

I am a good puppy.

I do not bite.

Feed me once a day.

Give me water to drink.

Keep my bed clean.

Thank you,
T.J. Brown

T.J. came from Uncle Harry. Uncle
Harry lived on a big farm.

Brett and Jerry took T.J. out of the box. He was happy to see the two little boys. He was happy to run and to play with them.

The boys were so happy that they jumped up and down. The puppy jumped up and down, too. He wagged his tail and barked his baby bark.

But when Father saw T.J., he said, "Oh, dear, what will we do with a dog in town?"

Father did not have a dog when he was a little boy. He did not like dogs, but Father looked at T.J., and T.J. wagged his tail. For the first time, Father liked a dog, but he did not say so right away.

"Oh, Father," said Brett, "please let us keep T.J. Jerry and I will take good care of him. We will give him water to drink. We will feed him every day. We will make him a good bed. We will wash him and keep him clean."

"T.J. will make a good watchdog," said Jerry. "See what big paws he has. He will grow up to be a big dog."

Father looked at Mother. Mother said, "I think this puppy will be good for Brett and Jerry."

Father looked at the puppy. Then Father looked at Brett and Jerry. Never had Brett and Jerry wanted anything so much as they wanted to keep that puppy.

"Well," said Father, "you may keep the puppy if you will look after him. He will have to learn many things. He will have to learn to be a good dog."

And that is how T.J. Brown came to live with Brett and Jerry.

T.J. and the Funny Smell

Brett and Jerry took good care of T.J. They fed T.J. his food once a day. They gave him water to drink. They made him a bed out of a box. They played with him every day. And T.J. grew.

When T.J. heard Brett and Jerry come home from school, he always wanted to play with them. T.J.'s bark grew. It was a big bark now. T.J.'s tail grew, and he wagged it and wagged it.

T.J.'s teeth grew, and he chewed and he chewed. He chewed the legs of the chairs and he chewed the legs of the tables. Then he chewed one of Father's new shoes.

Father said, "T.J. must go. A town is no place for a dog like T.J. It would be best if T.J. lived on a big farm."

Brett and Jerry did not know what to do. They gave T.J. some water to drink. They gave him some food. They put him to bed in his box. T.J. Brown was very happy. He went to sleep.

Brett and Jerry went to bed. They did not say anything, but they did not go to sleep right away because they were very unhappy.

In the night, T.J. woke up. His nose hurt. He got out of his box and he walked all around. He smelled a funny smell. It made his nose hurt very much.

T.J. barked and barked. He wanted Brett and Jerry to come and get him, but Brett and Jerry did not come.

T.J. wanted to go to Brett and Jerry, so T.J. pushed on the door. He pushed and he pushed and he pushed. He pushed the door open. T.J. barked and barked, but no one heard T.J. barking. Father and Mother and Brett and Jerry were fast asleep.

T.J. ran to the boys' room. He jumped up on the bed. Brett woke up. He smelled the funny smell. He called to Jerry. Jerry woke up and smelled the funny smell. It was smoke. They ran to Father's room.

"Get up, Father," cried Brett. "Get up."

"The house is on fire," cried Jerry. "The house is on fire."

And T.J. barked and barked.

Father smelled the smoke. He ran and called the firefighters. The firefighters came and put out the fire in the house.

One of the firefighters said to Father, "You had better thank that dog for getting you up."

"Yes, that is a very good dog," said Father.

"Is T.J. our dog for keeps?" asked Brett and Jerry.

"Yes, he is," said Father.

T.J. jumped up on Father and barked his big bark and wagged his big tail.

"Good dog," said Father.

"T.J. will always take good care of us," said Mother.

Brett and Jerry were very happy because T.J. was now their dog "for keeps."

Funny

One day, when Miko was only two years old, Father gave her a puppy. It was long and had brown hair, a long nose, and a long tail. Father put the puppy on the floor. Then Miko saw that it had four little, short legs.

Miko jumped up and down and laughed and laughed. "Funny, funny doggie," she cried.

And that was how Funny got his name.

One day Miko and Funny had been playing house in the backyard. Funny had been asleep in the doll bed. Then Funny woke up. He could not hear Miko laughing and talking to herself. Where was Miko?

Funny ran out of the playhouse and looked all around the yard. He did not find Miko. Then he saw that the gate to the backyard was open. Mother always shut the gate when Miko was playing.

Funny ran out of the gate. He looked up and down the street. He did not see Miko.

Down the street were the woods with big trees. Funny ran to the woods. He could see Miko playing in the woods.

Funny ran up to Miko and took hold of her blue dress with his teeth. He pulled and pulled to try to tell her that she must go with him. To Miko, this was a new kind of game. She laughed. She would not go with Funny. She ran away and went behind a tree.

Funny ran after Miko and barked. Miko laughed and ran behind a tree again. This was the best game that she and Funny had ever played together. Miko ran from tree to tree.

Soon Miko and Funny were far into the woods. Funny tried to get her to go with him, but Miko only laughed and pulled away.

Funny did not know what to do. If he went back to get help, Miko would be lost. The best that he could do was to stay with Miko.

Soon Miko got sleepy. She had been playing in the woods a long time. Miko found some grass under a big tree and went to sleep. Funny was right beside her, but he did not shut his eyes. He watched so that nothing would hurt Miko.

A squirrel came down from a tree and looked at Miko. Funny barked and the squirrel ran away.

A rabbit came out from behind a tree, and Funny barked again. The rabbit ran away. Funny would have liked to run after the rabbit, but he knew he must not go away from Miko. Funny would not let himself go to sleep. Little Miko was asleep just as if she were in her own bed at home.

Just as Funny could not keep his eyes open any longer, he heard something in the woods. Then he heard a man calling, "Miko, Miko."

Funny barked and barked.

Then the man called, "Funny, Funny, come here."

But Funny did not come. He just barked and barked. Funny could tell that there were many people in the woods.

They called, "Funny, Funny, come here," but Funny did not go away from Miko. He just barked and barked.

Then Funny heard Father calling, "Funny, Funny, where are you? Where are you, Miko?"

Funny ran to Father, barking and barking. Then he ran back to Miko. And Father found Miko asleep under the tree.

"Good dog, Funny," said Father. "If it had not been for you, we would not have found Miko."

Father took Miko in his arms and carried her. She opened her eyes and said, "Funny and Miko played a new game with the trees."

And then she went to sleep again.

Little Funny could not walk fast on his short legs. One of the people with Father picked Funny up and carried him. He said to Father, "This dog is not very big, but he is a brave little dog."

Funny did not know what a brave dog was. He saw that Miko was all right. And so he went to sleep.

Big Red

Big Red lived at Firehouse 66. He was called the "firedog," and all the firefighters liked him. When the fire truck went to a fire, Big Red was always sitting by the driver.

Big Red was a good firedog. He stayed with the firefighters. He kept boys and girls away from the fire so that they would not get hurt. When the fire was out, he jumped back on the truck. He sat by the driver for his ride back to Firehouse 66.

At the last fire, Big Red went right into the burning house. He barked to let the firefighters know that someone was in the house. They went into the house and found a little girl overcome by smoke.

Big Red was a brave dog to go right into the fire, but he had burned himself so badly that one of the firefighters had taken him to a doctor. The doctor said that the firefighters must take good care of Big Red so that he would get well.

One evening the firefighters were sitting down to their dinner when the firebell rang in Firehouse 66. The firefighters got up and ran to their places. Big Red thought he must go to the fire, too. He got up by the driver of the truck.

"Big Red," said the driver, "you cannot go with us today. We must take care of you, because you got burned in the last fire. Get down. You have to stay in the firehouse today."

Big Red got down off the truck. He was not happy. He did not know why the firefighters would not let him go to the fire with them. He saw the big truck go down the street, and then he went back into the firehouse. There was only one man left in the firehouse, and he stayed in the office.

Big Red walked around. He did not like to stay by himself. There was nothing for him to do. He was lonesome.

At first, he thought that he would go to his box and go to sleep. Then Big Red smelled something very good. It smelled like meat. Big Red thought that he would go and find out what smelled so good.

All this time the firefighters were putting out a fire at a store. It was just a little fire. It did not take the firefighters long to put it out. Then they went back to the firehouse.

The big truck was the first to get back. As the driver backed the truck into the firehouse, he saw Big Red. Big Red looked very happy.

"Hello, Big Red," called the driver. "You don't look lonesome at all. You look happy."

Big Red wagged his tail. He watched all the firefighters come back to Firehouse 66. He just sat and wagged his tail. He looked very, very happy.

When all the firefighters were back in Firehouse 66, they went back to their dinner. There were ten plates on the long table. When the firefighters had jumped up from the table to go to the fire, there had been some meat on every one of the ten plates. Now there were only two plates that had any meat on them.

The firefighters looked at Big Red. And Big Red just sat and looked at the firefighters and wagged his tail.

The meat had been very good.

Now when the bell rings in Firehouse 66, the men look to see whether Big Red is on the fire truck sitting by the truck driver. They do not want the dog to stay behind in the firehouse. When Big Red stayed behind in the firehouse, the firefighters had very little to eat when they got back from the fire.

Tootsie

All five of the children loved Tootsie, but Tootsie loved Mother best of all. When Mother read, Tootsie would sit beside her chair. When Mother was working, Tootsie would be with her. At dinner time, she would go to sleep under the table beside Mother's chair. And at night Tootsie would sleep in her basket right beside Mother's bed.

Tootsie's hair was all white. She was a very pretty little dog. She had learned to do many things. She could sit up. She could walk on her back legs. She would run after a ball and bring it back.

When Mother and Father and the five children went on a vacation, Tootsie went with them.

One day everyone in the car was very hot. Father stopped the car by a big river outside of a town. Everyone went in a store and had a cold drink, and Tootsie had a drink, too.

Then Father drove through the to the long bridge that was over the river. The man at the bridge asked for a dollar to let Father drive over the bridge. After they were over the bridge, Mother said, "Where is Tootsie?"

Father drove off the road and stopped. No one could find Tootsie. She was not in the car.

Eleanor said, "When we stopped for a drink, Tootsie got out of the car. I gave her a drink of water."

John said, "Tootsie and I were playing with a stick, but she stopped playing with me and ran over to where Marguerite was sitting on the grass."

Marguerite said, "I was drawing a picture and did not see Tootsie."

Catherine said, "When we got back into the car, I did not look to see whether Tootsie got into the car with us."

Edward said, "Tootsie is lost and we must go back and find her."

Father turned the car around. He drove back over the bridge. Again he had to give the man a dollar to go over the bridge. He drove through the town and stopped where they had had the cold drinks, but there was no Tootsie.

The children got out of the car. They asked everyone, "Did you see a little, white dog?"

One little boy said that he had seen a little, white dog running after a car. Little Tootsie could not run very fast. She could not keep up with a car.

One man said that there had been a little, white dog sitting under a tree beside the road right where the car had been. But Tootsie was not sitting under the tree now.

Someone had seen a little, white dog running up the road to a farmhouse.

Edward went with a little boy down the street that went into the town. Catherine and Marguerite started up the road away from the town to the farmhouse.

Eleanor and John walked up and down the streets calling, "Tootsie, Tootsie." The little, white dog could not be found.

Mother and Father sat in the car and waited. Mother thought that they would never see Tootsie again.

Pretty soon Eleanor and John came back to the car. They had not found Tootsie, and they had not found anyone who had seen a little, white dog. Eleanor cried, because she said that she would never see the little, white dog again.

Then John saw Marguerite and
Catherine coming down the road.
Marguerite was calling out and laughing.
Catherine was carrying a little, white dog
in her arms.

"We found Tootsie," called Marguerite.
"She went to the farmhouse to find someone
to look after her."

Tootsie was so happy to be with her
family again. She went to sleep in Mother's
arms.

"We will never let Tootsie get lost again," said Catherine.

"Well," said Father, "it is time we were getting started. We have a long ride in front of us."

"Where is Edward?" asked Mother.

"He went into town looking for Tootsie," said John. "A little boy had seen a little, white dog running after a car."

"Oh, dear," said Mother. "Edward will get lost. Does he know where we are?"

"There is nothing to do but wait and see whether Edward can find his way back to the car," said Father.

So everyone waited. Edward did not come back to the car.

"We will give him just a little longer," said Father. "If he does not come soon, we will ask the police to help us find him."

After a time, Edward came running back to the car. He saw Tootsie sleeping in Mother's arms. "I am so glad that Tootsie found her way back," said Edward.

"And I am so glad you found your way back, too," said Father. "We were going to ask the police to find you."

Everyone got into the car. Then everyone looked to make sure that Tootsie was in the car, too. Father drove through the town and to the bridge. He gave the man at the bridge a dollar to go over the bridge again. Three times in one day, Father had given the man at that bridge a dollar to drive over it.

"Tootsie," said Father, "think of all that money we had to give the man to ride over the bridge. But now we are together again and we are happy."

Chief, a Firedog

At one time, in every firehouse there lived a "firedog." The firedog ran to every fire. At night he slept in the room with the firefighters.

Mr. Joe Murphy had been a firefighter, but now he was retired. He lived in a little house by the sea. And with him lived his old firedog, Chief.

Mr. Murphy and Chief took long walks in the sun. They looked out over the sea, and sometimes they thought about fires they had helped put out in the town.

One day a big wind came up over the sea. The wind blew and blew. The wind blew down trees. The wind blew the sea water down the streets. Many houses were full of water. There were no lights anywhere.

Mr. Murphy and Chief sat in their little house. The wind blew all around them. The sea water was at their door. Chief cried and looked at Mr. Murphy.

"It is all right, Chief, old boy," said Mr. Murphy. "The wind will stop pretty soon. We have a good little house. Nothing is going to hurt us." Then Chief went to sleep at Mr. Murphy's feet.

As night came on, the wind went down. Mr. Murphy found two candles and lighted them. It was cold in the little house.

"Chief," said Mr. Murphy, "I think that we have an old oil heater. Now we must use it to keep us warm."

Mr. Murphy found the old oil heater. He found that there was some oil in it. He lighted the old oil heater and put it beside his chair. Then he sat down and tried to read a book by the light of the two candles.

Mr. Murphy grew very tired, because the candles did not give much light. Soon he was fast asleep in his chair.

Mr. Murphy heard Chief barking. Chief did not stop barking. He barked and barked. He took hold of Mr. Murphy's coat and he pulled and pulled.

Then Mr. Murphy woke up with a start. He smelled smoke. He saw that he had pushed the oil heater over in his sleep. Oil was all over the floor. It was burning and making black smoke.

Mr. Murphy had been a firefighter. He knew how to put out a fire. But if Chief had not barked and made Mr. Murphy wake up, the little house by the sea would have burned up.

Rags

The little, brown dog wanted someone to love him. His big black eyes watched the people who walked by. But no one looked at him, because he was not a pretty dog. His brown hair was too short, and his tail was too long. He walked on only three legs. One leg had been hurt by a car. There had been no one to care for him, and so the leg never got right again.

The little, brown dog was in a yard and he wanted to get out. So he got under the gate and ran down the street. He could run as fast on three legs as most dogs could run on four.

The little, brown dog ran down the street. He ran up to a man with a happy face. It was such a happy face that the little, brown dog stopped and jumped up on the man and barked.

The man stopped and looked at the dog. "You funny little Ragamuffin," said Tom Hilton. "Where is your home? Do they call you Rags?"

Rags jumped and barked. He tried to tell this kind man with the happy face that he wanted to stay with him.

"Rags," said Tom Hilton, "you must go home. I cannot play now. I am on my way to work."

Then Tom Hilton went on down the street, but Rags ran right behind him. Rags was not going to let this kind friend go. When Tom opened the door to a restaurant to get something to eat, Rags went in, too.

Rags sat at Tom's feet as quiet as could be, and pretty soon Tom put his hand down and gave Rags some meat to eat. It was the best dinner Rags had ever had.

One of the men in the restaurant said, "Hilton, what are you going to do with your dog when you fly the mail plane tonight?" Then the man gave Rags some more meat to eat.

Rags wagged his tail and barked to show how happy he was.

"I cannot get this dog to go away," said Tom Hilton. "He does not look like he has a home. Maybe I will have to take him flying with me tonight."

"Maybe he will bring you good luck," said the man.

"There are times when every airplane pilot could use a little good luck," said Tom Hilton.

Rags did not know what the men were saying, but they were kind. They gave him good things to eat. Rags was very happy.

When Tom Hilton left the restaurant, Rags was right behind him. Soon they got to the mail plane.

"Everything is ready to take off, Mr. Hilton," said Bill as he put the last of the mail on to the plane.

Tom Hilton got into the plane and looked to see that everything was all right. Rags jumped and jumped, but he could not get into the plane. Then Rags began to bark. His friend was going away and he wanted to go with him.

Tom Hilton looked out of the plane.

"Rags," he said, "you don't want to stay behind, do you? How would you like to fly the mail plane with me tonight? Hand him up, Bill, and I will take him with me."

And that is how Rags went on his first airplane ride. He thought it was a very funny ride. There was a big noise all of the time. Sometimes Rags thought he was going up and sometimes he thought he was going down. But he did not care as long as he was with Tom Hilton.

Rags went to sleep and when he woke up, the plane was on the ground. People were taking some of the mail out of the plane and putting more mail into the plane. One of the men said, "You are right on time, Hilton."

"Yes," said Tom Hilton, "the mail always gets here right on time. I will be flying over the mountains soon, but I will be right on time getting into New York City."

Rags cried a little, and Tom said, "So you woke up, Rags. Come get out of the plane, and we will get some milk to drink."

"That is a funny-looking brown dog you have with you," said one of the people.

"He is my good luck dog," said Tom. Then Tom went into the restaurant and got milk for Rags.

Rags and Tom got back into the plane. The noise started. They went up and up.

It was very dark. The noise went on and on. Rags was just about to go to sleep when he heard Tom say, "Well, what a time for that to go out. Here we are trying to get over the mountains, and I just cannot tell how far up we are flying."

Rags did not know the words, but he could tell things were not right. So he cried a little.

"Everything is going to be all right, Rags," said Tom. "We will just go up a little more so that we will get over the mountains."

The plane went up and up and up. Rags did not want to go to sleep now. The plane went on and on in the dark.

"Rags, I think we are over the mountains now. I think we can go down."

Rags wagged his tail in the dark, because he thought everything was all right with Tom.

Then down went the airplane. There was a great noise. The airplane hit something. Then the airplane hit the ground. The door came open, and Rags found himself on the ground. It was very dark, and Rags could not see a thing. He hurt all over.

Rags, the Hero

The mail plane had gone down at night in a field with trees all around it. Rags fell out of the plane.

Rags wanted to find Tom, the pilot. He walked around in the dark, but he could not find him. He hurt all over. He barked, but Tom did not come to him.

At last a little daylight came. Rags could see a great black thing that once had been an airplane. He thought that maybe Tom was over by this great black thing. He got up on his three legs and walked over to it. Then he found Tom in the grass. Tom did not move. Rags licked his face and his hands, but Tom did not open his eyes or say anything.

The sun was way up when Tom opened his eyes. Rags licked his face and barked.

"Well," said Tom, "where are we? I hurt all over. But you, little Ragamuffin, you are all right. We must both be lucky."

Rags did not know why Tom did not get up and walk. He barked and barked, but Tom did not move. Then Rags knew that something had happened to Tom.

Rags ran a little way through the woods, but he could find no one to help Tom. Then he ran back to Tom and licked his face.

"It is no use," said Tom. "I cannot move. Go get someone, Rags." Then Tom shut his eyes and did not open them again.

Rags ran through the woods. He found an old road. He ran down the road. He hurt all over, but he ran on and on. He saw a man and some horses in a field. Rags was afraid of the horses, but he ran to the man and barked.

"Where did you come from?" said the man. "Go on home."

Rags ran a little way into the woods. Then he ran back to the man and barked and barked, but the man could not tell what the dog wanted.

"Go home, little brown dog," said the man.

Rags ran back to where Tom was in the grass. Tom's eyes were shut. Rags licked Tom's face, but Tom did not open his eyes.

Then Rags heard some people coming through the woods.

"I heard it on the radio," said one of the men. "A mail plane did not get to New York City this morning. And they say that the pilot had a little, brown dog with him that he called his good luck dog."

"A little, brown dog came out of these woods this morning as I was working in the field," said the other man. "He barked and barked at me. I did not know what he wanted."

Rags barked and barked. Then the people soon found Tom Hilton in the grass.

"We must get this pilot to a doctor," said one of the people.

One of the people had a blanket. They put Tom on the blanket and carried him through the woods to a farmhouse.

Rags tried to walk with them, but he could not keep up. He hurt all over. Rags cried a little, and one of the people put him on the blanket with Tom.

When they got to the farmhouse, they called a doctor. The doctor came and took care of Tom. When Tom opened his eyes again, Rags was right there.

The first thing Tom said was, "Ragamuffin, now I know you are my good luck dog."

"Yes, Ragamuffin is your good luck," said the doctor. "You would have been done for if you had not been found."

Before long, people from a newspaper office came and took pictures of Rags and Tom. They called Rags a hero. But Rags did not care about being a hero. He was happy just being Tom Hilton's good luck dog.

The Ballplayer

When Carlos was ten years old, his big brother, Ben, gave him a black-and-white puppy for his birthday.

Big Brother Ben had said, "Shut your eyes and hold out your hands. I have a surprise for you." Then Ben had put the puppy into Carlos's hands.

"Take good care of him," said Ben. "When he grows up, make a good ballplayer out of him."

Ben was a ballplayer on the big team of the town, and Carlos thought that someday he himself would play ball as well as his big brother Ben. He would play on the big team, too.

Carlos named the puppy Spot. Carlos took good care of his puppy, and Spot grew into a big dog. By the time Carlos was a year older, Spot went everywhere that Carlos went.

When Carlos's birthday came around again, Ben gave Carlos a new ball and a bat.

"I want you to learn to be a good ballplayer," said Ben. "A good ballplayer has to learn to throw the ball. A good ballplayer has to learn to catch a ball. And a good ballplayer has to learn how to bat."

Ben showed Carlos how to throw and how to catch the ball, and he showed him a lot about how to bat the ball.

Carlos played ball with the boys at school, and he played ball with the boys after school. Carlos was always playing ball.

Now Carlos did not always catch the ball when it came to him. And Carlos did not always bat the ball where he wanted it to go. Carlos would say, "Spot, get the ball."

Spot would get the ball and take it to Carlos. And Carlos would say, "Good dog."

One day, Carlos got a letter from his big brother. It said,

Our team is going to play ball at home on Saturday. How would you like to see the game? You may sit with the players and bring us luck. This letter will let you into the ball park.
Your brother,
Ben

Carlos waited and waited until Saturday. He told all the boys at school that he was going to be with the team. He was going to bring them luck.

Then Saturday came. Carlos went with his letter that would let him into the ballpark. He sat with the players. He was going to bring Ben's team good luck.

But what about Spot?

Spot was very unhappy. Carlos had tied him in the backyard. He had said, "Be a good dog, Spot. I will be back soon."

Spot knew that it was time to play ball. Carlos always played ball on Saturday in the lot behind the house. How could Carlos play ball without Spot to help him?

Spot pulled and pulled on the rope on his collar. Then he bit the rope. He bit the rope again. Pretty soon, he bit the rope right through. He ran out of the backyard and ran to the lot behind the house. But there was no one there.

Where was Carlos? Spot ran on down the street looking for Carlos.

Spot had gone a long way when he got to the ballpark. Spot heard the people calling, "Play ball. Play ball."

Spot just ran through the gate into the ballpark. He looked around him and knew that this was a ball game.

Spot knew just what to do. He always helped Carlos play ball. Spot ran on the ball field. He watched the ball. He wanted to get the ball if it fell to the ground.

The people saw the little, black-and-white dog on the ball field. Everyone laughed.

Then Spot heard, "Get that ball. Get that ball."

Spot saw the ball on the ground. A man was running after the ball. But Spot could run faster than that man, so Spot got the ball. Spot ran down the field. He wished that he could find Carlos and give him the ball.

The people at the ball park laughed and laughed. Many men ran out on the ball field, but Spot would not let anyone catch him. He looked for Carlos, but he could not see Carlos anywhere.

Then Spot saw Ben. Spot ran to him and put the ball down at his feet. Ben picked Spot up and carried him off the field. He put the little, black-and-white dog into Carlos's arms.

"Hold your dog, Carlos," said Ben. "We cannot have a dog on the field." And then Ben laughed.

"Our team will have lots of luck now," he said. "We have a boy and a dog to bring us good luck."

A Medal for Billy

One day Billy got a letter. It was from the mayor of the town. The mayor asked Billy and his dog, Dandy, to see him on Saturday at three.

Billy asked his father about the letter, but Father only said, "Well, Billy, you and Dandy had better be there at three. You don't want to keep the mayor waiting."

Billy asked his Mother about the letter, and Mother said, "Oh, Billy, have you and Dandy done anything?"

"No, no," said Billy. "Dandy is a good dog. Sometimes I do have to tie him in the backyard to keep him from swimming across the river, but he never hurts anything."

Billy went out into the backyard to find Dandy. He sat down beside the big dog. Dandy put his paw on Billy's arm. Dandy wagged his tail. Then Dandy stopped wagging his tail and looked up into Billy's face. Billy did not look happy.

"Dandy, Dandy," said Billy. "have you done anything that I don't know about? I don't know what you do when you swim across the river. But you have not gone across the river for a long, long time now."

Billy's backyard went right down to the river, and Dandy liked to swim in the river. He liked Billy to throw a stick into the river. Then he would swim out and get the stick and take it back to Billy. Sometimes Dandy would swim across the river.

Billy and Dandy walked down to the river. "The river looks pretty now, Dandy," said Billy. "but it did not look pretty on the day of the big flood. That was the day the river tried to kill you."

Billy would never forget what happened on the day of the big flood. It had rained for days. He was going to school. He went into the backyard to tell Dandy good-bye.

The river was up to the grass in the backyard. Dandy ran up and down. He barked at the river. He would jump into the river and try to swim, but the river ran so fast that he could not swim very well. He would go back to the grass and bark at the river that was coming into his backyard.

Father went out into the backyard to look at the river.

"The river has been rising," said Father. "I wish that it would stop raining today. I would not like to see the river flood the town like it did when I was a boy."

"I have heard Grandmother tell how the water came right into the houses. I will not forget that story," said Billy.

"Yes," said Father. "The river went way over the road. But the new banks the people of the town have put by the river will keep the water from getting into our houses again."

"Dandy does not like the river to come into his yard," said Billy.

"You had better tie Dandy to his doghouse," said Father. "I am afraid that he will try to swim in the fast-running water."

Billy tied the rope that was on the doghouse to Dandy's collar and said to him, "Be a good dog, Dandy. We will go for a run as soon as I come back from school."

Dandy looked very unhappy. He went into the doghouse and went to sleep, and Billy went off to school.

At lunch time, it was raining so hard that the children did not go home. Mr. Jones came with a big basket of food. The children thought it was a lot of fun to eat lunch at school, but Mr. Jones and the teacher did not look like they thought eating lunch at school was fun at all.

Mr. Jones said to the teacher, "The river has been rising all morning, but the banks will hold. No water will get to us."

Billy heard what Mr. Jones said to the teacher. He thought how far up the river had been in his backyard when he left for school. He thought how his Grandmother had told him there had once been four feet of water in the house when the river had flooded its banks. And then Billy thought of Dandy tied to his doghouse.

Billy started for home. No one saw him go. He ran home through the rain. The water was up over the road near his house. Billy went right into the water. The water was deeper and deeper as he went around the house to the backyard.

"Dandy, Dandy," called Billy. "Where are you? Where are you?"

Billy did not hear anything but the noise of the water and the falling rain.

The water was deeper, but Billy went to the back of the house. Then he saw the doghouse in the water. And the doghouse

was coming at Billy. Dandy was tied to the doghouse, and Dandy was swimming to Billy as fast as he could swim. The big dog was very, very tired, because he had been swimming in the water for a long time.

Father never knew how Billy got Dandy and the doghouse out of the water and onto the road. As soon as Father found out that Billy was not with the other children at school, he too thought of Dandy tied to the doghouse. He knew where Billy had gone.

Father got into this car and went home as fast as he could. Sometimes the water was over the road, but Father got home.

There, sitting in the road beside the doghouse, was a very tired boy with his arms around a very tired dog.

Now Billy and Dandy looked at the river. "No, Dandy," said Billy again. "We will never forget that big flood."

Then Billy heard his Mother calling him. "Billy, you and Dandy had better get ready to go. You don't want to keep the mayor waiting."

"Come, Dandy," said Billy. "I have to take you into town with me. What do you think the mayor wants with us? I know you are a good dog, Dandy. Nothing the mayor can do to us will be like the time I had to get you and your doghouse out of the flood."

When Mother and Father and Billy and Dandy got to see the mayor, there was a big surprise for Mother and Billy. Father had known about the surprise all the time.

There were a lot of people that Billy knew. The mayor put a medal on Billy. Then the mayor said, "Billy, all of your friends want you to have this medal. You were very brave when you went into the water to help your dog, Dandy."

a
about
across
afraid
after
again
airplane
all
always
am
an
and
any
anyone
anything
anywhere
are
arm
arms
around
as
ask
asked
asleep
at
away
baby
back
backed
backyard
badly
ball
ballpark
ballplayer
banks
bark
barked

barking
basket
bat
be
because
bed
been
before
began
behind
being
bell
Ben
Ben's
beside
best
better
big
Bill
Billy
Billy's
birthday
bit
bite
black
blanket
blew
blue
book
both
box
boy
boys
boys'
brave
Brett
bridge

bring
brother
brown
burned
burner
burning
but
by
bye
call
called
calling
came
can
candles
cannot
car
care
Carlos
Carlos's
carried
carrying
catch
Catherine
chair
chairs
chewed
Chief
children
clean
coat
cold
collar
come
coming
could
cried

Dandy
Dandy's
dark
day
daylight
days
dear
deeper
did
dinner
do
doctor
does
dog
Doggie
doghouse
dogs
doll
dollar
done
don't
door
down
drawing
dress
drink
drinks
drive
driver
drove
eat
eating
Edward
Eleanor
evening
ever
every

everyone
everything
everywhere
eyes
face
falling
family
far
farm
farmhouse
fast
faster
father
father's
fed
feed
feet
fell
field
find
fire
firebell
firedog
firefighter
firefighters
firehouse
fires
first
five
flood
flooded
floor
fly
flying
food
for
forget

found
four
friend
friends
from
full
fun
funny
game
gate
gave
get
gets
getting
girl
girls
give
given
glad
go
going
gone
good
got
grandmother
grass
great
grew
ground
grow
grows
had
hair
hand
hands
happened
happy

hard
Harry
has
have
he
hear
heard
heater
hello
help
helped
her
here
hero
herself
Hilton
Hilton's
him
himself
his
hit
hold
home
horses
hot
house
houses
how
hurt
hurts
I
if
in
into
is
it
its

Jerry
Joe
John
Jones
jump
jumped
just
keep
keeps
kept
kill
kind
knew
know
known
last
laughed
laughing
learn
learned
left
leg
legs
let
letter
letters
licked
light
lighted
lights
like
liked
little
live
lived
lonesome
long

longer
look
looked
looking
looks
lost
lot
lots
love
loved
luck
lucky
lunch
made
mail
make
making
man
many
Marguerite
may
maybe
mayor
me
meat
medal
men
Miko
milk
money
more
morning
most
mother
mother's
mountains
move

Mr.
much
Murphy
Murphy's
must
my
name
named
near
never
new
New York City
newspaper
night
no
noise
nose
not
nothing
now
of
off
office
oh
oil
old
older
on
once
one
only
onto
open
opened
or
other
our

out
outside
over
overcome
own
paw
paws
people
picked
picture
pictures
pilot
place
places
plane
plates
play
played
player
players
playhouse
playing
please
police
pretty
pulled
puppy
pushed
put
putting
quiet
rabbit
radio
Ragamuffin
Rags
rain
rained

raining
ran
rang
read
ready
red
restaurant
retired
ride
right
rings
rising
river
road
room
rope
run
running
said
sat
Saturday
saw
say
saying
school
sea
see
seen
she
shoes
short
show
showed
shut
sit
sitting
sleep

Table of Contents

Jumbo

You all know that anything called "jumbo" is something big, such as jumbo peanuts. But do you know that Jumbo was the biggest elephant that ever came to the United States?

Jumbo was caught in Africa when he was a baby elephant. He went to live in the zoo in Paris, France. No one at the zoo thought that this little elephant was ever going to grow up to be the biggest and best-known elephant in the world.

When the baby elephant was older, he went to live in the zoo in London, England. The manager of the zoo in Paris had wanted one of the animals that lived in the London Zoo. So, the manager of the London Zoo gave the zoo in Paris an animal, and the London Zoo got the baby elephant.

Jumbo lived in the London Zoo for a long time. He was the biggest elephant in the zoo. Jumbo was more than ten feet high. He was very big and very strong.

Jumbo let the children ride in a big howdah, or seat, that was put on his back. Even the King and Queen of England had taken a ride in the howdah on Jumbo. The children of London thought of him as their very own elephant.

The manager of the London Zoo found that on some days, Jumbo was not very good and gentle. The manager was afraid that Jumbo might get to be a bad elephant. The manager knew that because Jumbo was so big and strong, they could not stop him if he was bad. He might hurt some of the children who came to the zoo.

For a long time, Mr. Barnum, who owned a circus in the United States, had wanted to buy Jumbo. He had many elephants in his circus. If he could buy Jumbo, his circus would have a bigger elephant that any other circus. The manager of the London Zoo thought that Jumbo might be happy in a circus with many other elephants, so he sold Jumbo to Mr. Barnum.

Jumbo was an African elephant. An African elephant is not like an elephant from India. African elephants do not like to be trained, so they are not used much in circuses. When Jumbo left for the United States, many things happened.

Jumbo Goes to the United States

When the time came for Jumbo to go to the United States, the manager of the London Zoo and the American bull-keeper who was to take him to the United States tried to get Jumbo into a box as big as a big room. Jumbo just lay down on the ground, and no one could make him move.

The next day a newspaper in London ran a story about Jumbo. The newspaper said, "Jumbo does not want to go to America. He lies on the ground and will not move. Jumbo loves the children of London. He likes them to ride in the howdah on his back. Jumbo does not want to go away from the children of London."

The children of London sent letters to the newspaper.

Please do not let our big elephant go away!
We love Jumbo.
We want to keep him in the London Zoo.
Patricia Smith

The newspapers in America ran the story about the big elephant that did not want to go away from the children of London.

Mr. Barnum, who owned the circus, was very happy about all of this. He wanted all the people in the United States to know that he had the biggest elephant that anyone had ever heard of.

The children of the United States sent letters to the newspaper in London.

We want to see the big elephant. Please send Jumbo to America.

Even the King and Queen of England did not want Jumbo to go away. They thought that the children of England must have Jumbo in the London Zoo.

Mr. Barnum sent a letter to the London newspaper.

We know that the children of London love Jumbo, but the children in America want to see the big elephant. And the children of America will love Jumbo, too. After a time, I will bring my circus to England. Then the children of London must be sure to come and see "the biggest circus in the world." And there they will see Jumbo.

The English manager and the American bull-keeper tried again to get Jumbo into the big box to go to America. This time they put the big box on wheels, like a wagon. Part of the wagon was in the ground, and the big box was left open at both ends. It was like a bridge. They put Jumbo's hay on this bridge.

Little by little, Jumbo learned to walk onto the bridge and eat. One day, when Jumbo was on the bridge and eating his hay, the ends of the big box were closed up. Jumbo was in the box.

The big box, which was on the wagon, was pulled out of the hole in the ground. Many big horses pulled the wagon down the road to the ship that would take Jumbo to the United States.

People came to say "Good-bye" to Jumbo because Jumbo was the King of the Elephants.

The big box was put on the ship for the United States. An English man from the zoo and the American bull-keeper had to be with Jumbo all the time to keep him quiet. When the ship got to the United States, many people went to the ship to get a first look at Jumbo.

The big box with wheels was taken off the boat. Many horses pulled Jumbo through the streets of New York City. A band in a wagon played music.

At first, Jumbo was afraid of the noise, the people, and the horses on the streets of New York City. But he got used to everything and was a good circus elephant.

The bull-keepers taught Jumbo many things. They taught him to walk at the head of the parade. There is an old picture that shows Jumbo reaching his trunk up to a window near the top of a house. A boy in the window is giving Jumbo a peanut.

Many, many people went to the biggest circus in the world to see the biggest elephant in the world.

Baby Elephants

At one time some movies were taken of wild elephants. The pictures were taken of a herd of wild elephants in India. In this herd, there were mother elephants and their babies. This story is about these elephant babies.

The first thing in taking movies was to get the elephants to a place where the people could take pictures. Many men of the country were sent out to go around the herd of elephants.

Slowly, slowly, using fire and noise, they moved the herd until they got them close to a river. At night the men sat by their fires, and the elephants did not go near them. An elephant is afraid of fire.

The elephants could get water at the river. The herd was still in the forest, but they could go out of the forest and down to the river to drink.

First, the big leader would go to the river. With his trunk raised high in the air, he would make sure that all was right. Then the big leader would go back into the forest.

Soon, two or three at the time, the herd of wild elephants went down to the river. At last, many elephants were in the river. There were baby elephants with their mothers. The old leader stood watching to see that everything was all right.

Once one of the baby elephants was under the water. The old leader went into the water and pulled the baby out with his trunk. He put the baby down at the side of the river.

The people taking the movies were across the river. They got some very good pictures of the wild elephants drinking and playing in the water. Best of all were the pictures of the mother elephants washing their babies and teaching them what to do in the water. The baby elephants liked playing in the mud and the water just like children do. It was lots of fun.

Then the people taking the movies wanted to take pictures of a herd of wild elephants being driven into a keddah, which is a big place with a high log fence all around it.

The men were going to drive the elephants across the river into the big keddah. The people taking the pictures were up in the trees all around the keddah.

The elephant drive started. The elephants rushed down to the river and started across. The mother elephants pushed the babies in front of them.

The elephants were afraid. They pushed against one another and made a great noise. And always the men moved the herd of wild elephants closer to the open gate of the keddah.

At last, the elephants were in the keddah, and such a noise you have never heard. The elephants tried to break out of the keddah by rushing against its sides, which were made of big logs. Everyone was afraid that the baby elephants in the keddah would be killed.

Then they saw one very small baby elephant fall in the mud. He would surely be killed because the elephants were rushing around and around in the keddah.

One of the men went between the logs of the high fence and into the keddah. He tied a rope around the leg of the baby elephant and pulled it out of the keddah.

Everyone went to see the baby elephant, and he was very afraid. He cried and cried. His mother in the keddah heard him. She tried to get through the side of the keddah, but she could not get out. So, she cried and cried for her baby.

The baby was given water to drink, but he did not know how to get the water into his mouth. A baby elephant does not know how to use its trunk to drink. Its mother has to teach it how to drink.

Some of the men pushed the baby down to the river. He did not want to go, so he made a lot of noise. At last, the men got him into the river, and there he got a good drink of water.

After the baby elephant had a drink, he ran back to the side of the keddah. He could hear his mother call him.

The movies had been taken, and it was time to let the herd of wild elephants out of the keddah. They would go back to their forest. But no one knew what would happen to the little baby elephant. Maybe his mother would not take him back because he had the smell of people on him.

At first, when the gates of the keddah were opened, just one or two elephants left and went to the river. The little baby went to the gate. Maybe he heard his mother call.

More elephants rushed out of the keddah. They rushed to the river and went across to their home in the forest. Then, the rest of the herd rushed out of the keddah.

Everyone thought that the little elephant would be killed. But when the dust had gone away, there was the little baby elephant waiting at the gate of the keddah.

Out of the keddah rushed the last elephant, the big leader of the herd. His trunk was high in the air. He ran to the river and down into it.

With a loud squeal, the little baby elephant ran to the river and started to cross. His little head went up and down in the water. Pretty soon he went around and around in the water.

Then some of the men pushed a boat into the river. They put a rope around the little elephant and pulled him across the river. Then the men left him on the ground, and the baby elephant went to sleep.

The men watched over the baby, but they did not go near him. They knew that his mother would not take him back if he had the smell of people on him.

During the night, the mother elephant went down to the river and got her little baby. She took him away with her into the forest, and all the people were very happy.

The Flies and the Brooms

It was a very hot day. The elephants in the circus were practicing, but they were very hot and not doing well. The elephants were not happy. They kept moving their feet and their tails and their big ears. The bull-keeper was having a hard time getting the elephants through their tricks. At last he stopped to rest.

Flies were everywhere; and if there is one thing that elephants don't like, it is flies. Elephants cannot get flies off their backs. An elephant's trunk will not reach over its back. An elephant's tail is not long enough to get the flies off its back.

In the forest, a wild elephant coats itself with mud, and then the flies cannot hurt it. But in the circus tent, there is not a way to get away from the flies.

The elephants stopped practicing, but they kept on moving their tails and their trunks and their ears. They were hot and tired, and the flies were everywhere.

A man who sold toys and peanuts at the circus stopped to talk to the bull-keeper. He had a lot of toy brooms. These brooms were to be sold to the children at the circus.

The leader of the elephants raised her trunk and made a big noise. Then she went over to the man with the brooms and put her trunk around him. He called to the bull-keeper to make the elephant go away, but the big elephant would not go away. She made a noise by blowing air through her trunk.

The bull-keeper knew that the big elephant was trying to tell him something. At first, he did not know what it was. Then, he laughed.

"I think that the elephant wants one of your toy brooms," said the bull-keeper, and he had to buy one of the brooms and give it to the elephant.

The elephant took the broom in her trunk. She reached over her back. With the broom, she could reach every part of her back and get the flies away.

Then all of the other elephants raised their trunks. They made a great noise. The bull-keeper had to buy a broom for each elephant.

All day long the elephants had their brooms. They paraded through the streets of the city, each elephant holding its toy broom. They did their tricks in the circus, each holding its toy broom. They would not put their brooms down until night came and the flies went to sleep.

I think that those elephants were pretty smart. Don't you?

A Joke on Mother

Beautiful was a big mother
elephant, and Beautiful had a baby
elephant. This little elephant got into
everything. He went with his mother
and played around her while she
worked. He loved to play with children.

The children loved the baby
elephant. They sometimes gave him
peanuts, which he liked very much.
Sometimes in play the baby elephant ran

after the children. He was big and they were little, but he never hurt them.

The mother, Beautiful, worked hard pulling big logs from the river. To do this, she had a great band around her to which a pulling chain was fastened. A chain was put around the log in the river, and the end of this chain was fastened to the pulling chain on the elephant. A helper fastened the two chains together with a hook. The person who took care of the elephant sat on the elephant's head. He told her just what to do. The big elephant would pull and pull, until she got the log out of the river.

Beautiful would rest for a while. Then she would pull and pull again to get the big log over the grass and the mud.

While Beautiful worked pulling logs, her baby played beside her. She would talk to him as elephants do.

One day the baby elephant got tired of playing. He walked to his mother's side, watching her pull the big log. His mother pulled and pulled. The big log slowly moved across the grass and through the mud. Then his mother stopped and rested with the air blowing through her trunk.

When his mother stopped, the baby elephant looked at the chain that was on the log. He looked at the chain that was on his mother. He had never really looked at them before. He looked very carefully at the funny hook that kept the two chains together. This was something very funny, and it moved when he pulled it with his trunk. So, baby elephant pulled out the hook that kept the two chains together.

With his trunk, baby elephant took
hold of the chain that was on Beautiful.
After she had rested, she started to pull
and pull again, but it was baby elephant,
not the log, that she was pulling.

Baby elephant thought that this was more fun than he had ever had. Soon his trunk got tired, and he let go of the chain. Over went Beautiful on her head, and her rider fell to the ground.

Beautiful got up and looked around. She did not see a big log behind her, but she saw her baby elephant. Then she knew that her baby had played a trick on her, and baby elephant knew that he had done something very bad.

Baby elephant knew that his mother was going to hit him with her trunk. He gave a squeal and ran off into the forest.

Beautiful did not run after him, because she had work to do. She helped her rider get up onto her back again. Then they went to find the big log. The rider's helper put the chains together again, and Beautiful pulled the big logs.

That night when Beautiful was eating, her baby went back to her. He looked just like any little boy who knows that he has done something bad. Baby elephant knew that Beautiful would punish him before he could have anything to eat.

Beautiful hit the baby elephant with her trunk. Baby elephant squealed and squealed. I think that he said to his mother, "Mother, Mother, I will be good. I will never again unfasten the chains when you are pulling a log."

And the baby elephant never did.

A Tusker Looks After His Rider

Everyone must think. You have to think about things around you. You have to think what is the best thing to do. It is the way you think that makes you who you are. Elephants can think, also.

Some elephants and their riders were helping make a bridge across a river. The bridge was nearly finished. There were only three big logs that had to be lifted up to finish the bridge.

A big tusker, an elephant with tusks, who had his rider on his head, was going to put the last three logs on the bridge. It was time to eat, and the rider wanted to get the work finished.

The rider told the tusker to pick up the log with his tusks, hold it with his trunk, then lift his head high, and use his trunk to put the log on the bridge.

But the big, gray elephant was
afraid to do what the rider wanted. He
could tell that when he lifted his head
high the big log was going to roll back
toward his head. He knew the log was so
big that he could not hold it with his
trunk.

His rider, whom he loved very much, sat on the elephant's head. If the log rolled back, the rider would be killed. So the tusker put down the log. His rider was very angry with him.

The big elephant looked all around the ground, and his rider did not know what he was doing. At last the tusker found what he wanted. It was a piece of wood.

The big elephant picked up the piece of wood with his trunk and pushed it hard between his tusks. When the elephant picked up the big log with his tusks and lifted his head, the log could not roll back toward the rider because the piece of wood would stop it.

One at a time, the big tusker lifted the last three logs onto the bridge. Then with his trunk he took out the piece of wood between his tusks and threw it away. Now it was time to eat. And I am sure that the big tusker was given something very good to eat that night.

Anyone who knows about elephants can tell many stories about how elephants think.

Tusko Helps Himself

The Great Tusko was in the Barnes Circus. Tusko was not trained to work with other elephants because he did not seem to like other elephants. He walked at the head of the circus parade with his bull-keeper riding on his head.

Everyone had heard of the Great Tusko. Everyone wanted to see the "biggest elephant in America." Tusko was the biggest elephant then because Jumbo had died.

The bull-keeper had to be very careful with Tusko. He never knew what would make Tusko angry. When Tusko was walking at the head of the parade, he was always chained to an elephant named Ruth.

Ruth was a strong elephant and a good elephant. If Tusko tried to run away, Ruth would pull back on the chains and stop him.

There was always a bull-keeper beside Tusko because no one knew what Tusko might do.

One day the elephants were going back to the circus lot after the parade. Tusko was walking slowly. He was chained to Ruth, but he was walking behind her, and his bull-keeper was walking beside Ruth.

Suddenly, Tusko stopped. He saw a man with a big basket of hot dogs. Tusko thought that he would like some. He picked up the hot dogs with his trunk and put them into his mouth. He ate the hot dogs as fast as he could because he knew that he was being bad. He knew that his bull-keeper would stop him.

The man with the hot dogs shouted and tried to make the big elephant go away. It was a good thing that the bull-keeper was so near. If Tusko got angry with the hot-dog man, he might have hurt him. The circus paid the man for his hot dogs.

The circus had to pay for many things Tusko did. Once time Tusko ran away and mashed the front of a house. The circus had to pay for it.

But Tusko was a very smart elephant. Sometimes he was very good and helped his bull-keeper.

Once Tusko was riding in a wagon that was being pulled by a car. It was very hard on Tusko because the wagon moved from side to side. The man turned the car too fast. Tusko fell over, and the wagon fell over, too.

Now, how would you get a big elephant out of an overturned wagon?

The bull-keeper went to Tusko and talked to him. "Big boy," said the bull-keeper, "I am going to help you get out of this, but you are going to have to help me."

Tusko seemed to know what the bull-keeper was saying.

The bull-keeper got into the overturned wagon. He got under Tusko's big feet. If Tusko had moved at all, he would have killed the bull-keeper. But Tusko lay quietly. The bull-keeper took the chains off Tusko's feet. Then he got him out of the overturned wagon.

Tusko stood still while the bull-keeper put the chains back on his feet. Then when the wagon and the car were all right, Tusko walked back to the wagon. He knew that his bull-keeper would take care of him.

a
about
across
afraid
Africa
African
after
again
against
air
all
also
always
am
America
American
an
and
angry
animal
animals
another
any
anyone
anything
are
around
as
at
ate
away
babies
baby
back
backs

bad
band
Barnes
Barnum
basket
be
beautiful
because
been
before
behind
being
beside
best
between
big
bigger
biggest
blowing
both
box
boy
break
bridge
bring
broom
brooms
bull
but
buy
by
call
called
came
can

cannot	drinking
car	drive
care	driven
careful	during
carefully	dust
caught	each
chain	ears
chained	eat
chains	eating
children	elephant
circus	elephants
circuses	elephant's
city	end
close	ends
closed	England
closer	English
coats	enough
come	even
could	ever
country	every
cried	everyone
cross	everything
day	everywhere
days	fall
did	farm
died	fast
do	fastened
does	feet
dog	fell
dogs	fence
doing	fenced
done	find
don't	finish
down	finished
drink	fire

fires	happy
first	hard
flies	has
for	have
forest	having
found	hay
France	he
from	head
front	hear
fun	heard
funny	help
gate	helped
gates	helper
gave	helping
gentle	helps
get	her
getting	herd
give	high
given	him
giving	himself
go	his
goes	hit
going	hold
gone	holding
good	hole
good-bye	home
got	hook
grass	horses
gray	hot
great	house
ground	how
grow	howdah
had	hurt
happen	I
happened	if

in
India
into
is
it
its
joke
Jumbo
Jumbo's
just
keddah
keep
keeper
keepers
kept
killed
king
knew
know
known
knows
last
laughed
lay
leader
learned
left
leg
let
letter
letters
lies
lift
lifted
like

liked
likes
little
live
lived
log
logs
London
long
look
looked
looks
lot
lots
loud
love
loved
loves
made
make
makes
man
manager
many
mashed
maybe
me
men
might
more
mother
mothers
mother's
mouth
move

moved
movies
moving
Mr.
much
mud
music
must
my
named
near
nearly
never
new
New York City
newspaper
newspapers
next
night
no
noise
not
now
of
off
old
older
on
once
one
only
onto
open
opened
or

other
our
out
over
overturned
own
owned
paid
parade
paraded
Paris
part
parts
pay
peanut
peanuts
people
person
pick
picked
picture
pictures
piece
place
play
played
playing
please
practicing
pretty
pull
pulled
pulling
punish
pushed

put
queen
quiet
quietly
raised
ran
reach
reached
reaching
really
rest
rested
ride
rider
riders
rider's
riding
right
river
road
roll
rolled
room
rope
run
rushed
rushing
Ruth
said
sat
saw
say
saying
seat
see

seem
seemed
send
sent
she
ship
shouted
shows
side
sides
sleep
slowly
small
smart
smell
so
sold
some
something
sometimes
soon
squeal
squealed
started
still
stood
stop
stopped
stories
story
streets
strong
such
suddenly
sure

surely
tail
tails
take
taken
taking
talk
talked
taught
teach
teaching
tell
ten
tent
than
that
the
their
them
then
there
these
they
thing
things
think
this
those
thought
three
threw
through
tied
time
tired

to
together
told
too
took
top
toward
toy
toys
trained
trees
trick
tricks
tried
trunk
trunks
trying
turned
tusker
Tusko
Tusko's
tusks
two
under
unfasten
United States
until
up
use
used
using
very
wagon
waiting
walk

walked
walking
want
wanted
wants
was
washing
watched
watching
water
way
we
well
went
were
what
wheels
when

where
which
while
who
whom
wild
will
window
with
wood
work
worked
world
would
you
your
zoo